Under The Moon

poems selected by
Pie Corbett and Valerie Bloom

the
eagle

He clasps the crag with crooked hands;
Close to the sun in lonely lands,
Ring'd with the azure world, he stands.
The wrinkled sea beneath him crawls;
He watches from his mountain walls,
And like a thunderbolt he falls.

Alfred, Lord Tennyson

AUTUMN BIRDS

The wild duck startles like a sudden thought,
And heron slow as if it might be caught;
The flopping crows on weary wing go by,
And greybeard jackdaws, noising as they fly;
The crowds of starlings whizz and hurry by
And darken like a cloud the evening sky;
The larks like thunder rise and suther round
Then drop and nest in the stubble ground;
The wild swan hurries high and noises loud,
With white necks peering to the evening cloud.
The weary rooks to distant woods are gone;
With length of tail the magpie winnows on
To neighbouring tree, and leaves the distant crow,
While small birds nestle in the hedge below.

John Clare

Flamingo

Not a word! not a word
Under the moon
When the glass of the blue lagoon
Is stirred,
And out of the reeds
In her scarlet weeds
 Steps the Flamingo.
A flame in flower,
A flower in flame,
As bright and brilliant
As her name,
 Princess Flamingo.

Radiant head!
Fantastic grace!
Delicate tread
That leaves no trace.
Before the moon
Sinks out of sight
She will take her flight
From the blue lagoon,
 Princess Flamingo.

Eleanor Farjeon

The Wild Swans at Coole

The trees are in their autumn beauty,
The woodland paths are dry,
Under the October twilight the water
Mirrors a still sky;
Upon the brimming water among the stones
Are nine-and-fifty swans.

The nineteenth autumn has come upon me
Since I first made my count;
I saw, before I had well finished,
All suddenly mount
And scatter wheeling in great broken rings
Upon their clamorous wings.

I have looked upon those brilliant creatures,
And now my heart is sore.
All's changed since I, hearing at twilight,
The first time on this shore,
The bell-beat of their wings above my head,
Trod with a lighter tread.

Unwearied still, lover by lover,
They paddle in the cold,
Companionable streams or climb the air;
Their hearts have not grown old;
Passion or conquest, wander where they will,
Attend upon them still.

But now they drift on the still water,
Mysterious, beautiful;
Among what rushes will they build,
By what lake's edge or pool
Delight men's eyes when I awake some day
To find they have flown away?

W. B. Yeats

HAWK ROOSTING

I sit in the top of the wood, my eyes closed.
Inaction, no falsifying dream
Between my hooked head and hooked feet:
Or in a sleep rehearse perfect kills and eat.

The convenience of the high trees!
The air's buoyancy and the sun's ray
Are of advantage to me;
And the earth's face upward for my inspection.

My feet are locked upon the rough bark.
It took the whole of Creation
To produce my foot, my each feather:
Now I hold Creation in my foot

Or fly up, and revolve it all slowly –
I kill where I please because it is all mine.
There is no sophistry in my body:
My manners are tearing off heads –

The allotment of death.

For the one path of my flight is direct

Through the bones of the living.

No arguments assert my right:

The sun is behind me.

Nothing has changed since I began.

My eye has permitted no change.

I am going to keep things like this.

Ted Hughes

The Robin's Song

I am cheerful. You can
Depend on me. I'm around
All the year. In the rain,
When frost is on the ground
Or the sun is dancing, I'm here,
Bright in colour and sound.

Other birds are less stout,
Sing flawless songs in Spring,
Look more beautiful, there's no doubt.
I am always pleased when you fling
Crumbs to me. Yes, I am happy.
Isn't that everything?

Elizabeth Jennings

Haiku Triptych

A tiny green frog
sits upon a lily pad
idly moongazing

Near by a brown moth
on finding a nice streetlight
boogies all night long

Inside a small boy
hypnotized by the TV
bathes in its blue haze

James Carter

Goodnight

The click of a switch.
In his glass bowl the gold snake
is at once asleep.

Pamela Gillilan

Goodbye

And so
as evening falls
I close the curtains on
the empty bed. And shadows creep
inside.

Valerie Bloom

Triad

These be
Three silent things:
The falling snow ... the hour
Before the dawn ... the mouth of one
Just dead.

Adelaide Crapsey

The Warning

Just now,
Out of the strange
Still dusk . . . as strange, as still . . .
A white moth flew. Why am I grown
So cold?

Adelaide Crapsey

Silver Aeroplane

Silver aeroplane
Speeds across the summer sky
Leaving in its wake
Trails of vapour: white scribblings
On a page of blue paper.

John Foster

Things That Go 'Bump' In The Night

Things that go 'bump' in the night,
Should not really give one a fright.
It's the hole in the ear
That lets in the fear,
That, and the absence of light!

Spike Milligan

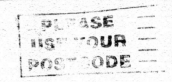

Postcard from Fairyland

Spell-binding scenery.
Lots of moonbathing,
(no tan).
Food delicious,
portions small.
Elves quarrelsome.
Was granted three wishes –
messed it up.
So home Thursday.

Gerard Benson

Postcard from Three-Bear Cottage

Not much of a holiday.
The furniture is broken.
Daddy Bear booms all the time –
Baby Bear squeaks.
Nothing to eat but porridge.

Gerard Benson

Football Training

Monday
Practised heading the ball:
Missed it – nutted the neighbours' wall.

Tuesday
Perfected my sideline throw:
Fell in the mud – forgot to let go!

Wednesday
Worked on my penalty kick:
A real bruiser – my toe met a brick.

Thursday
Gained stamina – went for a jog:
Ran round in circles – lost in the fog!

Friday
Developed my tactical play:
Tackled the goal post – it got in the way.

Saturday
Exercised – twenty-eight press-ups:
Did pull a muscle – but no major mess-ups.

Sunday
At last – the day of the match!
Came through it all without a scratch.
The ref was amazed how I kept my nerve;
He agreed it's not easy to be the reserve!

Celia Warren

Circus Lion
Gives Evidence

At crack of whip
I jumped through
hoops of fire.
And the people loved it.

All that clapping.
All those lights
just for me, a king
who did as he was told.
One day each clap became a roar
that filled my ear.
Each light fell
like a moon on a forest floor.
My mane flared
with old remembrances
till I was full of
myself. Full of Lion.

Then, ladies and gentlemen,
came the final trick.
And you know the rest.
At blast of trumpet
he put his head into
the kingdom of my mouth
which I closed forever.

He was a good man, my trainer.

John Agard

Song in Space

When man first flew beyond the sky
He looked back into the world's blue eye.
Man said: What makes your eye so blue?
Earth said: The tears in the oceans do.
Why are the seas so full of tears?
Because I've wept so many thousand years.
Why do you weep as you dance through space?
Because I am the mother of the human race.

Adrian Mitchell

HAVE YOU READ?

Enjoy Your Homework	*by R. U. Joking*
Out for the Count	*by I. C. Stars*
Cliff-Top Rescue	*by Justin Time*
A Year in Space	*by Esau Mars*
Your Turn to Wash Up	*by Y. Mee*
Off to the Dentist	*by U. First*
Broken Windows	*by E. Dunnett*
Pickpocket Pete	*by M. T. Purse*
Lions on the Loose	*by Luke Out*
Helping Gran	*by B. A. Dear*
Ten Ice Creams	*by Segovia Flaw*
Rock Concert	*by Q. Here*

Judith Nicholls

I Saw A Jolly Hunter

I saw a jolly hunter
With a jolly gun
Walking in the country
In the jolly sun.

In the jolly meadow
Sat a jolly hare.
Saw the jolly hunter.
Took jolly care.

Hunter jolly eager –
Sight of jolly prey.
Forgot gun pointing
Wrong jolly way.

Jolly hunter jolly head
Over heels gone.
Jolly old safety-catch
Not jolly on.

Bang went the jolly gun.
Hunter jolly dead.
Jolly hare got clean away.
Jolly good, I said.

Charles Causley

Who?

Who is that child I see wandering, wandering
Down by the side of the quivering stream?
Why does he seem not to hear, though I call to him?
Where does he come from, and what is his name?

Why do I see him at sunrise and sunset
Taking, in old-fashioned clothes, the same track?
Why, when he walks, does he cast not a shadow
Though the sun rises and falls at his back?

Why does the dust lie so thick on the hedgerow?
By the great field where a horse pulls the plough?
Why do I see only meadows, where houses
Stand in a line by the riverside now?

Why does he move like a wraith by the water,
Soft as the thistledown on the breeze blown?
When I draw near him so that I may hear him,
Why does he say that his name is my own?

Charles Causley

Duncan Gets Expelled

There are three big boys from primary seven
who wait at the main school gate with stones
in their teeth and names in their pockets.
Every day the three big boys are waiting.
"There she is. Into her boys. Hey Sambo."

I dread the bell ringing, and the walk home.
My best friend is scared of them and runs off.
Some days they shove a mud pie into my mouth.
"That's what you should eat," and make me eat it.
Then they all look in my mouth, prodding a stick.

I'm always hoping we get detention.
I'd love to write 'I will be better' 400 times.
The things I do? I pull Agnes MacNamara's hair.
Or put a ruler under Rhona's bum and ping it back
till she screams; or I make myself sick in the toilet.

Until the day the headmaster pulls me out,
asking all about the three big boys.
I'm scared to open my mouth.
But he says, "you can tell me, is it true?"
So out it comes, making me eat the mud pies.

Two of them got lines for the whole of May.
But he got expelled, that Duncan MacKay.

Jackie Kay

the past

The girl I was is out at sea.
Isn't that funny? She just walks
further and further away, slowly.

Soon I'll think we had different lives
me and her, her and me.
Maybe I'll wave to her across the sea,

lift my arm high above my shoulder
and wave to the wee girl with the black curly hair,
her skirt way above her knees in the dark sea.

Jackie Kay

Nettles

My son aged three fell in the nettle bed.
'Bed' seemed a curious name for those green spears,
That regiment of spite behind the shed:
It was no place for rest. With sobs and tears
The boy came seeking comfort and I saw
White blisters beaded on his tender skin.
We soothed him till his pain was not so raw.
At last he offered us a watery grin,
And then I took my hook and honed the blade
And went outside and slashed in fury with it
Till not a nettle in that fierce parade
Stood upright any more. Next task: I lit
A funeral pyre to burn the fallen dead.
But in two weeks the busy sun and rain
Had called up tall recruits behind the shed:
My son would often feel sharp wounds again.

Vernon Scannell

Grannie

I stayed with her when I was six then went
To live elsewhere when I was eight years old.
For ages I remembered her faint scent
Of lavender, the way she'd never scold
No matter what I'd done, and most of all
The way her smile seemed, somehow, to enfold
My whole world like a warm, protective shawl.

I knew that I was safe when she was near,
She was so tall, so wide, so large, she would
Stand mountainous between me and my fear,
Yet oh, so gentle, and she understood
Every hope and dream I ever had.
She praised me lavishly when I was good,
But never punished me when I was bad.

Years later war broke out and I became
A soldier and was wounded while in France.
Back home in hospital, still very lame,
I realized suddenly that circumstance
Had brought me close to that small town where she
Was living still. And so I seized the chance
To write and ask if she could visit me.

She came. And I still vividly recall
The shock that I received when she appeared
That dark cold day. Huge grannie was so small!
A tiny, frail, old lady. It was weird.
She hobbled through the ward to where I lay
And drew quite close and, hesitating, peered.
And then she smiled: and love lit up the day.

Vernon Scannell

Index of Titles